welcome

It's my pleasure to welcome you to the Natural History Museum. We have been on this site in South Kensington for over 130 years and we are home to one of the world's most important natural history collections. Behind the scenes, hundreds of scientists maintain and develop the collections, undertaking research that increases our understanding of nature and applying this knowledge to issues that affect us all – from the control of malaria to the sustainable use of the world's resources.

Every year, about five million people come to explore the treasures we look after, or simply to enjoy the wonderful building we are proud to occupy. It is you – our visitors – who help make the Natural History Museum what it is today. We hope you will take home some of our passion for the beauty and wonder of the natural world – and our commitment to protect it.

Above all, we want your visit to be an exciting and memorable experience. Please give us your feedback, and stay in touch with us via our website www.nhm.ac.uk or our Membership scheme.

Thank you for visiting. I hope to welcome you back very soon.

Dr Michael Dixon
Director of the Natural History Museum

a gallery of life

Come and explore the world-famous Natural History Museum in South Kensington, London. Since 1881 this glorious building with its blue and honey-coloured terracotta façade has held Britain's treasured natural history collections. They are an irreplaceable record of our planet's astonishing diversity, currently about 70 million specimens strong – and growing. Discover the beautiful, the rare and the sometimes weird. You'll find exciting exhibitions, specimens to touch and scientists to talk to. Take a walk in the Wildlife Garden or relax over coffee with Chi-Chi the panda. This is a place for everyone, expert or amateur, to explore the natural world on which we all depend.

We are many things

Only a fraction of the millions of specimens we care for are on show. Behind the scenes lie kilometre after kilometre of shelving stacked with specimens in alcohol, from microscopic worms to formidable Komodo dragons. There are cupboards packed with pressed plants and freezers of frozen DNA. There are storerooms of skeletons from three-metre-long whale skulls to tiny boxes of fish bones, insects, historic maps, manuscripts and artworks, fossils, plants, minerals and meteorites.

Among them are objects collected by some of the most famous names in natural history, and from the great voyages of discovery that opened up the natural world to westerners. There are fish and flowering plants from Captain James Cook's voyage on the *Endeavour* and maps belonging to geology pioneers Charles Lyell and William 'Strata' Smith.

The ever-growing collections are part of a global model of Earth's diversity, and it's our job at the Museum to look after them. They are an international resource for science, studied by the 300 scientists who work here and many visiting experts.

The seed is sown

The Museum owes its existence to a wealthy London doctor, naturalist and collector, Sir Hans Sloane (1660–1753). As a young man, Sloane's life was changed forever when he went to work as the Governor of Jamaica's physician in 1687. During 15 months spent there, he carefully recorded the island's natural history, returning to London with hundreds of plant and animal specimens.

By the time he died in 1753, Sloane had amassed 80,000 objects and books. Ranging from natural history to archaeology, the collection filled his London home. He left it all to the nation in his will, and this was the seed of the British Museum in Bloomsbury. The collections were added to over the years, and in 1881 the natural history section was moved to a museum of its own, what is now the Natural History Museum in South Kensington.

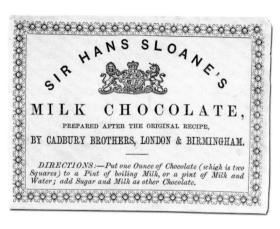

Sir Hans Sloane (1660–1753)

Sloane rose to become President of the Royal Society, and royal physician. But his public claim to fame is as the man who successfully marketed drinking chocolate in Britain. The Spanish had originally brought chocolate to Europe more than 100 years before, but it was Sloane who popularised it in Britain. While in Jamaica, he noticed local people brewed a bitter drink from the beans of the cocoa tree. Finding it 'nauseous', he added hot milk and sugar and so created drinking chocolate. The scientific name for cocoa is *Theobroma cacao*. *Theobroma* means 'drink of the gods' although drinking chocolate was first sold as a medicine.

a temple to nature

Many people walk into the Natural History Museum and ask what it was before it was a museum. It feels like a cathedral, but what cathedral has prehistoric creatures staring down from the roofs, or monkeys climbing the columns? In fact this building was purpose-built in the 1870s as a brand new museum to house the nation's natural history collections. It came about after a campaign by a man called Sir Richard Owen, and was designed by the brilliant young architect Alfred Waterhouse.

A new home

Sir Hans Sloane's collection may have been the foundation of the British Museum, but the man who helped create a new home for the natural history collections in South Kensington was eminent scientist Richard Owen, superintendent of the British Museum's natural history departments. He watched as specimens poured in from the colonies all over the world, as Britain's empire was expanding fast. The British Museum's natural history collections began to grow, eventually becoming overcrowded and showing signs of neglect. Owen believed the world's most powerful nation should have the world's biggest and best natural history museum. He wanted a new museum for them to showcase all the new discoveries, and the glory of God – to his mind, their creator.

The man who named the dinosaurs

Sir Richard Owen (1804–1892) was one of Europe's greatest authorities on skeletal anatomy. He famously identified the giant moa (left) from only a fragment of leg bone. In 1842, he announced the discovery of a whole new group of extinct reptiles, which he called the dinosaurs (from the Greek for terrible lizards). It was a bold step, as only three species had been recognised in England at that time. Owen was, however, a vocal and vicious opponent of Charles Darwin's theory of evolution. But, even as he was planning the Museum, ideas about evolution were beginning to take hold. While Owen continued to claim that all species were separate creations, evolutionists saw them as connected through time by common ancestry.

The building is crawling with animals living and extinct, such as lions (left) and pterosaurs (right).

Inspired by nature

Alfred Waterhouse was a relatively unknown architect when he inherited the project to design the Natural History Museum in 1866, after the original architect died. He created one of the finest Victorian buildings in England, using a round-arched, decorated Romanesque style, influenced in part by visits to German cathedrals.

The Museum is believed to be the first building to be clad inside and out with the beautiful combination of honey and pale blue terracotta, made from baked clay. Terracotta was cheap and easy to clean, and could be used to form wonderful mouldings of plants and animals to decorate the Museum, inside and out. The decorations reflect Owen's plan to divide the Museum displays rigorously between past and present, with living creatures to the west, fossils, rocks and minerals to the east. On columns and arches, birds and mammals peer out from foliage, while octopuses and fish float in rippling waves.

Nature on the move

Moving the natural history collections to South Kensington took more than a year. Last to arrive, in late 1882, were the zoological collections – a move that took 97 days and 394 trips by horse and cart. Among them were 52,000 fragile glass bottles holding fish and other animals preserved in highly flammable methylated spirit. A special secure building had to be built for them at the back of the Museum. In 2002, these collections were moved again to a safer, environmentally controlled building called the Darwin Centre. By then, they numbered 22 million items.

The largest move in the Museum's history was yet to come. In 2005 about 28 million insect and spider specimens were packed up and the 1930s building that housed them was demolished to make way for their new home, the second part of the Darwin Centre (see page 12).

> ❝ The walls and ceiling are decorated as befits a Palace of Nature. ❞
>
> *The Times*, 1881

The terracotta decorations were cast from models based on original drawings made by Alfred Waterhouse (above).

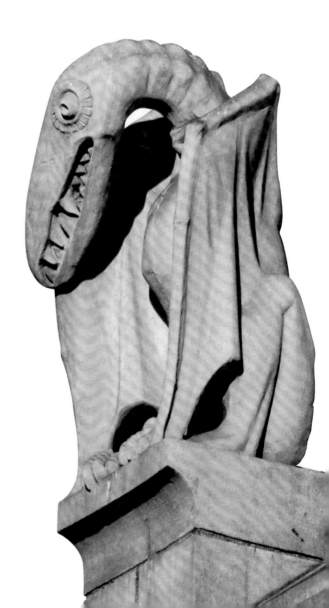

the world collected

Behind the scenes, the collections at the Museum are breathtaking. The 70 million individual specimens represent virtually all groups of plants and animals, past and present, and include the rocks and minerals that make up our planet. Six million books, journals, manuscripts, maps and artworks are a further treasure trove of knowledge. Together, they are an unrivalled database of our planet's past and a resource to help conserve its future.

Global heritage

The collections, libraries and archives are world-renowned for their diversity and historic importance. There are specimens collected 400 years ago, and eighteenth-century paintings recording creatures no European had ever seen before. There are fossils of single-celled organisms from the beginnings of life on Earth and meteorites made of material as old as the solar system.

Why collect?

Before the nineteenth century, it was fashionable to collect curious objects such as unusual shells or fine mineral crystals. Explorers returning from all corners of the world brought back natural objects to eager private collectors. Discoveries built up as European empires expanded, and collecting became more systematic and organised. As well as finding economically useful products, scientists wanted to build a catalogue of Earth's diversity – a record of the beauty and strangeness of nature.

The Museum cares for more than 8,500,000 butterfly and moth specimens.

Collections were increasingly used as a tool for science, a means of understanding the natural world. From the 1860s, evolutionary theory revolutionised research. Collections could be used to show how life on Earth had changed over time, and how species were related (for example, how our own species is related to other apes). It became important to collect not just one specimen of a species but many, to capture the full range of variation and enable us to determine what species truly exist.

Fossil frog, *Rana pueyoi* – you can see not only its skeleton, but also the preserved outline of its body.

Can anything be a specimen?

A specimen can be anything from the mounted skins you see in the galleries to bits of bone, teeth and hand-sized samples of rock and minerals. Some are more curious, such as handbags made of crocodile skin, beetles turned into jewels and shells engraved with prayers. Today, there are also slides of tissue and frozen samples of DNA. Even sounds can be specimens. The more we know about a specimen, the more scientifically valuable it is. The information contained in our Library and Archives is essential as it helps bring the specimens to life, underpinning the scientific work we do.

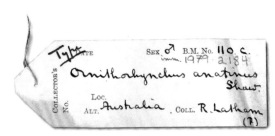

Snipe fly in Baltic amber, about 35 million years old.

The first of their kind

For every named species, one specimen is chosen as the 'type', and acts forever as the dictionary definition of what that species is. Anyone researching a species, or trying to separate out a new one, must refer back to the type. We hold nearly half, 850,000, of the world's type specimens, and some are very unusual – the 1901 African okapi type specimen is a belt made from hide from its striped hindquarters. Sometimes, when nothing remains at all, the type is a written description of a species or even artwork.

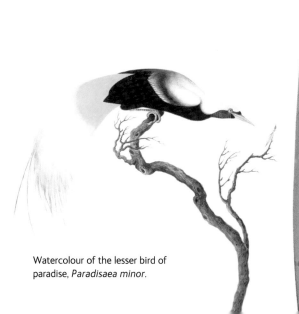

Watercolour of the lesser bird of paradise, *Paradisaea minor*.

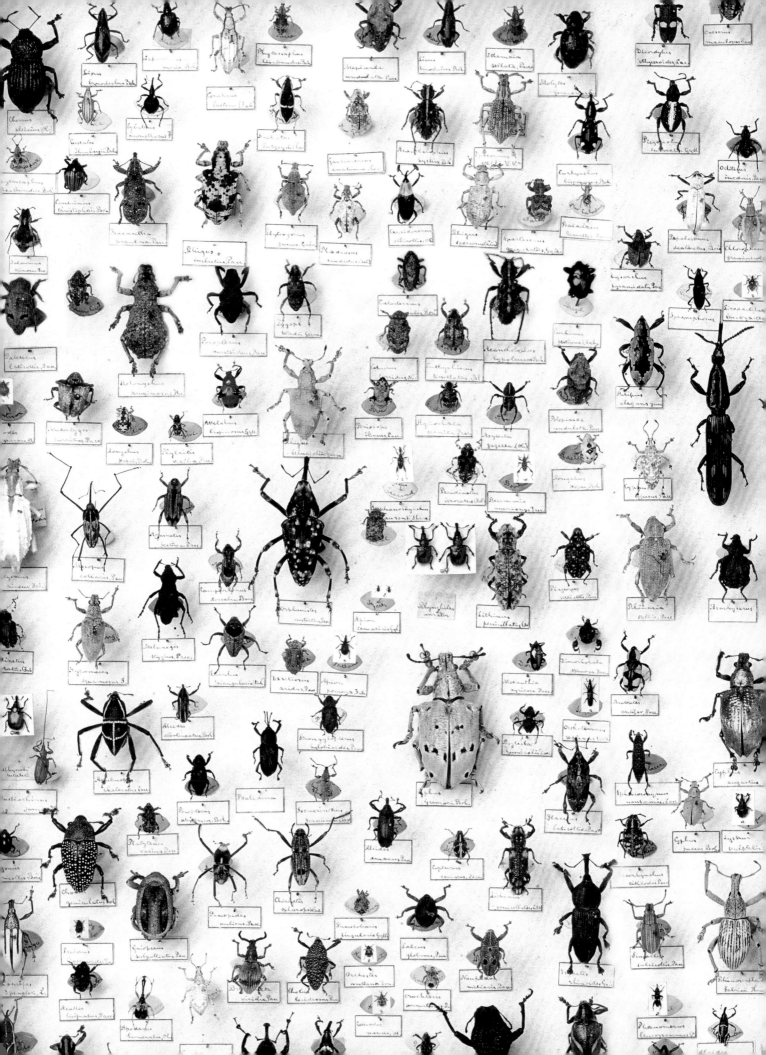

we never stop learning

There's even more to us than the millions of specimens kept here. We are a world-class research centre, with experts on anything from snails to space, working to uncover the secrets of the unique collections we hold. We acquire an average of 150,000 new specimens each year and our loans to other institutions comprise more than 57,000 specimens. More than 300 scientists work here, with collaborators in 70 countries across the world. Ten thousand researchers come to use the collections every year.

Unravelling the secrets of life

Museum scientists are making important discoveries about our planet, its present diversity and the processes generating that diversity. Our botanists, for example, are working with colleagues in Mexico and USA to build the *Flora Mesoamericana*. This is the first full description of all the flowering plants, ferns and their relatives growing in the southernmost states of Mexico and Central American republics. In Russia, zoologists are examining the microscopic life of Lake Baikal, the world's largest and deepest lake, to understand how life has adapted and evolved in this unique isolated environment. Palaeontologists are investigating the early occupation of Britain by humans going back 900,000 years. Mineralogists are using the information locked in volcanic rocks to learn what is happening under the Earth's surface.

Helping the planet

The knowledge our scientists generate can help meet real-life challenges: developing new resources and using existing ones more wisely, protecting our health and our environment. Our entomologists are looking for ways to distinguish mosquitoes that carry deadly malarial parasites from seemingly identical ones that don't. Our mineralogists are investigating how minerals behave in the soil to track and minimise the spread of pollution from mines or waste dumps. And in the mountains of Central America, data from satellite images combined with data from vegetation surveys can help foresters to manage and conserve tropical forests. Our scientists also play a vital role in providing reliable species data to help better conserve our wildlife.

There are more species of beetle in the world than species of any other organism.

Working with you

The Museum draws on the enthusiasm of the public by involving them in projects such as contributing records to a survey of cherry trees across the UK. Anglers also help our scientists by monitoring changes in river insect populations. From gardeners to forensic scientists, our staff deal with more than 10,000 enquiries each year from the public and organisations that need specimens identified through the Angela Marmont Centre (see page 15).

The future will reveal more

Collections and records can always reveal new information, whether it's discovering an undetected species in an old collection or using new techniques such as DNA analysis or CT scanning to reveal previously unseen details. Many collections still await study.

Our scientists go to great lengths for their research, such as collecting samples from the forest canopy in an inflatable platform suspended from a small airship.

The need for a name

Our core work is to identify, name and classify species. Each is given a unique scientific name, so that people throughout the world using different languages can refer to it without confusion. For living things, this has two parts: the genus (a small group of closest relatives) followed by the unique species name. Our genus is *Homo* and our species is *sapiens*. Species and genera are grouped again within larger categories to express wider relationships. Lions, *Panthera leo*, and leopards, *Panthera pardus*, are grouped with other cats, the cats with dogs and other carnivores. These in turn are classified as mammals, and so on.

hintze hall

Our dramatic Hintze Hall is an exhibit in itself. Light streaming in through the high windows picks out details in its terracotta decorations, stained glass and mosaic floor. Wide, round-arched bays along each side house some of the many treasures held here. The star of the show is the dinosaur *Diplodocus*, its extraordinarily long neck stretching out to greet visitors as they enter.

Dinosaur centre stage

You can't miss *Diplodocus* in the grand space of the Hintze Hall. Known affectionately as Dippy by staff, it's a full-size replica of an original 150-million-year-old skeleton in the Carnegie Museum of Natural History, Pittsburgh, USA. It arrived in 36 crates, and is a giant jigsaw of 292 bone casts, including 70 vertebrae in the tail. When the cast was unveiled at the Museum on 12 May 1905, it instantly became an icon. It was the first full skeleton of a sauropod dinosaur to go on display in the world.

At 26 metres, *Diplodocus* is one of the longest dinosaurs so far discovered. It's a sauropod, a type of gigantic plant-eating dinosaur characterised by a very long neck and tail, barrel-shaped body and pillar-like legs.

For years, the *Diplodocus* tail was displayed dragging on the ground. But in 1993, after new research showed that these dinosaurs probably carried their tails well clear of the ground to counterbalance the great neck, we had it lifted up.

Charles Darwin awaits visitors at the top of the first flight of stairs.

Wonders at different scales

Running the length of the Hintze Hall are eight alcoves, known as wonder bays, four on either side. In each you'll find wonders of the natural world. There's a huge *Glyptodon*, an extinct relative of today's armadillos with an armoured barrel body, and a fish-like ichthyosaur from Jurassic seas. A woolly mammoth skull from Ilford, the only complete skull ever found in Britain, looks you straight in the eye.

Other treasures are more delicate: a lace-like mass of gold freed from its surrounding quartz, fossil sea lilies frozen as if still waving in the current. A tiny spider is displayed caught in amber, and you can marvel at the exquisite paper architecture of a wasp nest. Looking out over the entire hall from the grand staircase is a 2.2-tonne marble statue of Charles Darwin. It replaced a statue of the Museum's founder Richard Owen for Darwin's 200th birthday celebrations in 2009.

Living fossil

A coelacanth floats in its preservative bath, its body bleached by the fluid to a ghostly beige. In life this chunky fish is deep blue, spotted with white. What makes it so special is that it was thought to be extinct, known only from fossils. Then, in 1938 a South African scientist recognised one among the catch of an Indian Ocean trawler, and in 1998 a second species was discovered in Indonesia. Among its many un-fish-like features are limb-like fins and a hinge in the top of the skull, increasing the gape of its jaws to swallow large prey. People used to believe coelacanths were the missing link between fish and land animals, but this is no longer thought to be true.

darwin centre

The newest addition to the Museum is the state-of-the-art Darwin Centre, a vast laboratory and storage facility for the Museum's entomology, zoology and plant specimens. At its heart is a 65-metre-long, eight-storey-high cocoon, which visitors spiral through to see how scientists collect, store and research specimens. Four virtual guides – real scientists at the Museum – point the way, introducing you to the different areas. At the entrance, is a beautiful glass case crammed with more than 100 specimens, from huge elephant beetles to tiny sandflies. Hundreds more are on display inside, and behind the scenes lie 20 million others. There are interactive games and challenges all along the way. Test your skills of sorting butterflies into groups, the same way scientists do to build the tree of life. Or play a DNA sequencing game to control the spread of malaria. Watch video diaries from scientists out in the field, to hear how they collect specimens. Then play a game to see how well you would prepare for work on the icy plains of Siberia, or deep into uncharted rainforest.

The Darwin Centre reveals the hidden world of scientific research. About 200 Museum scientists work here on cutting-edge research into the big questions about nature, such as why are there so many kinds of living thing, how are they all related and what threats do they face? Through viewing decks, video and intercom, you can enjoy a snapshot of these once concealed spaces. See where scientists extract, process, sequence and analyse DNA.

The spirit of conservation

Spirit is the common name for industrial alcohol (methylated spirits). It keeps specimens in good condition for a long time, and is especially good for soft-bodied specimens such as whole fishes and snakes. Despite extensive research, no one has found anything better at an affordable price.

A microphone in the specimen sorting area lets you talk directly to them about their work that day. They could be pressing plants collected from the streets of London or sorting through thousands of beetles fresh from the jungles of Central America.

At the entrance to the centre is a beautiful glass display of plants, insects and arachnids, plus interactive screens with plenty of take-home information.

Collections still hold secrets

Museum zoologists use the spirit collections for their research in biodiversity and medicine. New techniques, like molecular biology, can extract vital information, such as DNA, from even the tiniest fragments of a specimen. Each organism has a unique DNA sequence and the sequences of closely related species are similar. Our scientists can use them to tell apart species that look very similar, like mosquitoes. Only some of the 3,500 species of mosquito carry the malaria parasite, which is responsible for three million deaths wordwide each year. Targeting the mosquitoes that carry the parasite is one way of reducing these deaths. But different species need different control methods. DNA sequencing can swiftly identify the species so we can select the best method for controlling the mosquitoes and slowing the spread of malaria.

There are other, untapped treasures – 20,000 jars of plankton samples collected from the Antarctic Ocean in the 1920s to 1950s remain unsorted. They are a priceless resource for future research.

Apart from pubs, the Darwin Centre is one of the few buildings in London to have alcohol on tap.

The Sloane Herbarium

In a secure, climate-controlled area in the Darwin Centre is a most precious legacy. Sir Hans Sloane's collection of 120,000 pressed and dried plants, vegetables and 'vegetable substances', reflect his early interest in herbal medicines and plants in general. The herbarium has been consulted by many great botanists including the Swedish botanist Carl Linnaeus (1707–1778). Linnaeus's modern system of classification was a major turning point in botanical science. Leaf through some of the highlights of the Sloane Herbarium with the turning pages interactive.

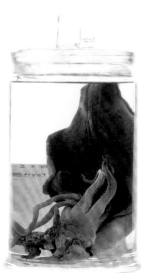

Angela Marmont Centre

On the lower ground floor of the Darwin Centre is a special place for anyone wanting to take their natural history interest further. The Angela Marmont Centre for UK Biodiversity has a team of experts that welcomes, by appointment, amateur naturalists, enthusiasts and other societies studying British wildlife to investigate UK animals, insects, plants, fossils and minerals.

A place to research

There's a reference collection of more than 10,000 drawers packed with bumblebees, ferns, ammonites, shells and more. Four thousand of those drawers hold just butterflies and moths. You can find out how to join a citizen science project, such as the water and seaweed surveys, using the NaturePlus kiosks or through the Open Air Laboratories network (OPAL).

If you need reference materials there's a UK natural history library, and there's a space for workshops and meetings. If you've found a strange bug in your bananas or something crawling around on the beach that you've never seen before, the Identification Advisory Service has dedicated staff to help identify them. Just drop in with your find and an identification enquiries officer will start the detective work.

The Darwin Centre's giant cocoon protects vital plant and insect collections, which go back 400 years.

Interact with scientists in the Attenborough Studio on the Darwin Centre's ground floor.

The Attenborough studio

For fun, live shows with scientists or to watch spectacular films, the Attenborough Studio on the ground floor is the place to be. This modern 64-seater amphitheatre is fitted with big screens and the latest technology so you can enjoy stunning computer-generated visuals while learning about life on Earth. It's an amazing place to come and hear scientists talking about their work, during one of the daily Nature Live talks. There's a host for each event, who'll interview the scientist then open it out to the floor so that everyone has the chance to ask the questions. Some events, like the weekend Animal Vision family show, involve real animals, while others clue you up on the latest news, like when there's been a natural disaster.

In between the daily talks, shows and events, you can catch the interactive film Who Do You Think You Really Are?, a revealing story of evolution from Earth's early history using large-screen projection, personal handsets and webcams. Or catch one of three 15-minute films made with the BBC Natural History Unit, including David Attenborough: Life on Camera.

wildlife garden

Step outside the Darwin Centre and follow the signs to the Wildlife Garden – the Museum's first living exhibition of the countryside where you can walk through woodland, past meadow, ponds and heathland. The garden is open between April and October and at other times on request. Special seasonal events for visitors of all ages take place at various times during the year, including themed weekends such as the Bat Festival held in partnership with the Bat Conservation Trust, Insect Day and Hedgerow Harvest, with workshops and displays as well as opportunities to meet Museum scientists and learn more about the garden's biodiversity. On most days during the summer term the garden is also a living classroom where students can investigate pond life and explore habitats.

Created from scratch

Opened in July 1995 the Wildlife Garden was designed and planted to illustrate a range of British semi-natural habitats including meadow, chalk downland, ponds, woodland, hedgerow and heathland. Volunteers play an important part in the care of the garden and help with planting, pruning, composting and coppicing to ensure that each habitat and plant community retains its special qualities.

The Wildlife Garden in the Museum is home to many plant and animal species.

An oasis for nature

Despite its position alongside one of London's busiest roads, wildlife in the garden has thrived. A surprising number of species have made their home there. While frogs and newts were introduced deliberately, other animals came in of their own accord. Blackbirds, wrens, robins and long-tailed tits enjoy the security of mixed hedges to nest in and feed from, and many other birds use the garden as a seasonal stopover. On summer evenings pipistrelle bats pursue mosquitoes and mayflies.

 More than 350 beetle species and more than 500 species of moth have been recorded in the garden.

The Jersey tiger moth is a colourful arrival in the garden.

Seasonal changes

Spring comes early to the Wildlife Garden and some birds, such as long-tailed tits, are preparing to nest as early as February. Later, primroses, bluebells and wild garlic bloom in the woodland, and frogs and newts mate in the pond. By summer, moorhens are feeding their young, while dragonflies and damselflies hunt over the water. The chalk downland area is a mass of flowers, including wild marjoram, lady's bedstraw and orchids.

Autumn brings toadstools – more than 150 species of fungi have been recorded. Birds fly in to feed on the bright berries. In winter the garden seems still, but beneath the fallen leaves life continues and spring plants start producing their first foliage.

Our greyface Dartmoor sheep, brought in to graze the chalk grassland and meadow areas, are a popular sight.

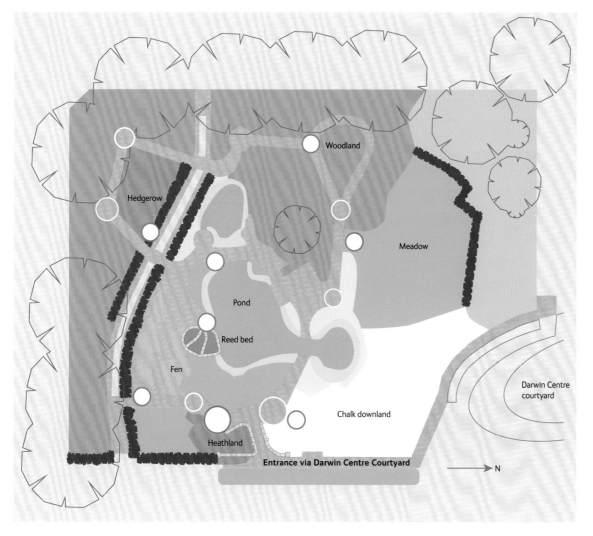

The map shows all the different habitats that have been created to attract a variety of wildlife in an urban environment.

Woodland

Hedgerow

Meadow

Pond

Reed bed

Fen

Chalk downland

Darwin Centre courtyard

Heathland

Entrance via Darwin Centre Courtyard

N

treasures – cadogan gallery

Venture behind the beautiful stained glass windows at the top of the main stairs and you find a gallery of icons. Treasures is an intimate celebration of the Museum's collection, 22 specially selected objects that are either unique, valuable, famous or surprising. The low-lighting and elegant display cases create an atmosphere of contemplation, where each object is treated like a jewel. Together they tell the story of the human endeavour to understand the world around us.

Either side of the gallery, just outside, sit the largest of the objects on display: the awesome Guy the gorilla, London Zoo's most popular animal, and a giant moa, a towering extinct bird from New Zealand.

What makes this gallery unique is the use of digital screens to tell the story, taking you deeper into who discovered each object and what it has revealed about our world.

The chosen few

Selecting just a few objects from a collection of 80 million specimens was a mammoth task, but each is special in its own way. They were chosen from a long list from the earth and life sciences at the Museum – palaeontology, botany, zoology, mineralogy and entomology. They include specimens from the voyages of discovery by Darwin and Cook, and bones from the ill-fated dodo. There are also rocks from beyond our planet, such as the oldest surviving meteorite discovered in the UK, formed during the birth of the solar system 4.6 billion years ago, and a piece of moon rock presented to the Museum by President Nixon. There's the first Neanderthal skull discovered, the first *Iguanodon* teeth ever found and a rare first edition of Darwin's *On the Origin of Species*. One of three penguin eggs brought back from the Antarctic by Captain Scott's tragic polar expedition is on display, collected to help prove that birds and reptiles were related although the theory was later dismissed. There's also the first *Archaeopteryx* that was found, one of only 10 specimens known worldwide of probably the earliest known bird.

Nautilus

Carved by Johannes Belkien in the late 1600s, this nautilus shell comes from Sir Hans Sloane's collection. As a naturalist, physician and successful entrepreneur, Sloane used his wealth to build a collection that formed the core of the British Museum, and subsequently the Natural History Museum as well. The nautilus is considered a living fossil, having remained relatively unchanged since the appearance of its ancestors 350 million years ago. Today the nautilus suffers from overfishing due to the continuing popularity of its shell's distinctive shape and lustre.

PLATE CCXVII

Drawn from Nature by J.J.Audubon, F.R.S. F.L.S.

Engraved, Printed & Coloured, by R.Havell, 1834.

Louisiana Heron. ARDEA LUDOVICIANA; Wils. *Male adult.*

Birds of America

Artworks form a huge part of the Museum's collection, and one of the most spectacular has been brought out for display in Treasures, a metre-long page from *The Birds of America* by John James Audubon (1785–1881). The hand-coloured prints were full of drama and life, pictured life-size in their natural habitats. The stuffed specimens painted by his contemporaries looked lifeless and unnatural by comparison. The artwork on display is changed monthly to prevent light damage.

Dodo

This rare dodo skeleton is constructed from bones that are from different individuals and are around 1,000 years old. Just 90 years after their discovery by humans in the late 1500s, dodos were extinct. To investigate the origins of this unusual bird, the Museum's first superintendent Richard Owen intercepted some rare dodo specimens that were being sent to a potential rival, and thus the bones became part of the Museum's collection.

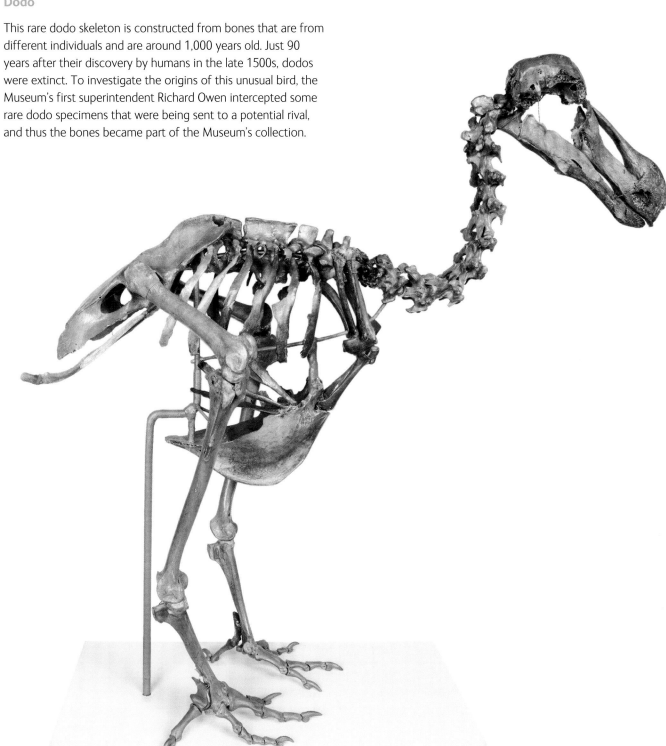

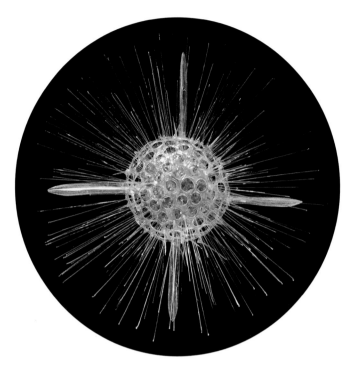

Emperor penguin egg

The embryo inside this emperor penguin egg was extracted with the hope that by studying it the missing link between birds and reptiles might be discovered. Edward Wilson, chief scientist of Captain Scott's 1910 expedition to Antarctica, walked 100 kilometres in complete darkness at -40°C to retrieve eggs from what was then the only known breeding colony. The three eggs that survived the journey were cut open, their embryos removed and pickled. By the time of their eventual study in 1934, the theory responsible for their collection had been dismissed.

On the Origin of Species

This first edition of Darwin's *On the Origin of Species* was published in 1859. In it Darwin describes his theory of evolution by means of natural selection. Despite the controversy surrounding the theory at the time, the book sold out the day it was published. Its success may have in part been due to its conversational rather than academic writing style. Darwin was galvanized into publishing earlier than planned after receiving a letter outlining a similar theory from fellow naturalist Alfred Russel Wallace.

Blaschka glass models

This exquisitely accurate glass model of a radiolarian was made by Leopold Blaschka and his son Rudolph between 1876 and 1889. Leopold was inspired to recreate marine creatures in glass after a long sea voyage. Ranging from octopuses to microscopic plankton, the Blaschkas' work was popular with museums, which had previously struggled to display these creatures as the animals lack backbones, and so tended to sink to the bottom of their display jars. No one has been able to replicate the Blaschkas' techniques.

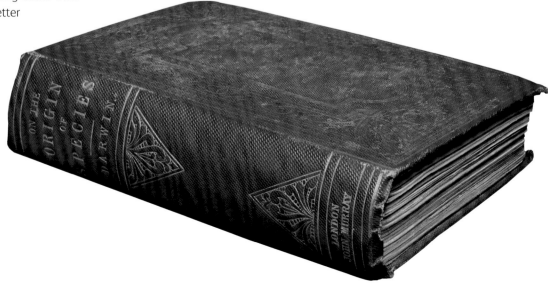

plant power

High above the Hintze Hall, on the second floor landing, stands one of our most impressive exhibits, a single massive slice taken from a giant sequoia, one of the world's largest trees. From here, if you make the long climb, you're rewarded with a wonderful bird's-eye view of the hall and a closer look at its magnificent painted ceiling.

Giant sequoia

When living, this tree stood at more than 60 metres, taller than the Museum's tallest tower. We know it was 1,300 years old when it was cut down: someone counted all its growth rings. The trunk is marked with some famous events in British history, from the Battle of Hastings in 1066 to the Battle of Trafalgar in 1805. It was a seedling in 557, and 500 years later was already more than two metres wide. Uncut, it might have continued growing for another 1,000 years – these are some of the largest and longest living trees in the world. Remarkably, they grow from seeds no bigger than a grain of wheat.

The five-metre-wide slice comes from a tree felled specially for the Chicago World Fair in 1893, when such trees were more common than today. They now occur only in the Sierra Nevada Mountains of central California and are highly protected. Nowadays it would be unthinkable to cut one down just for an exhibition.

Don't forget to look up

From the landing you can enjoy a clear view of the magnificent painted ceiling panels, part of the original Waterhouse design. They are made up of a series of 162 panels of flowering plants, painted by Messrs Best & Lea of Manchester. At this end of the hall, above the landing, you can see plants that were of great economic importance to the British Empire, such as coffee and cotton. In the main part of the hall, the plants are more stylised. Those at the apex are most richly decorated to draw your eye upwards.

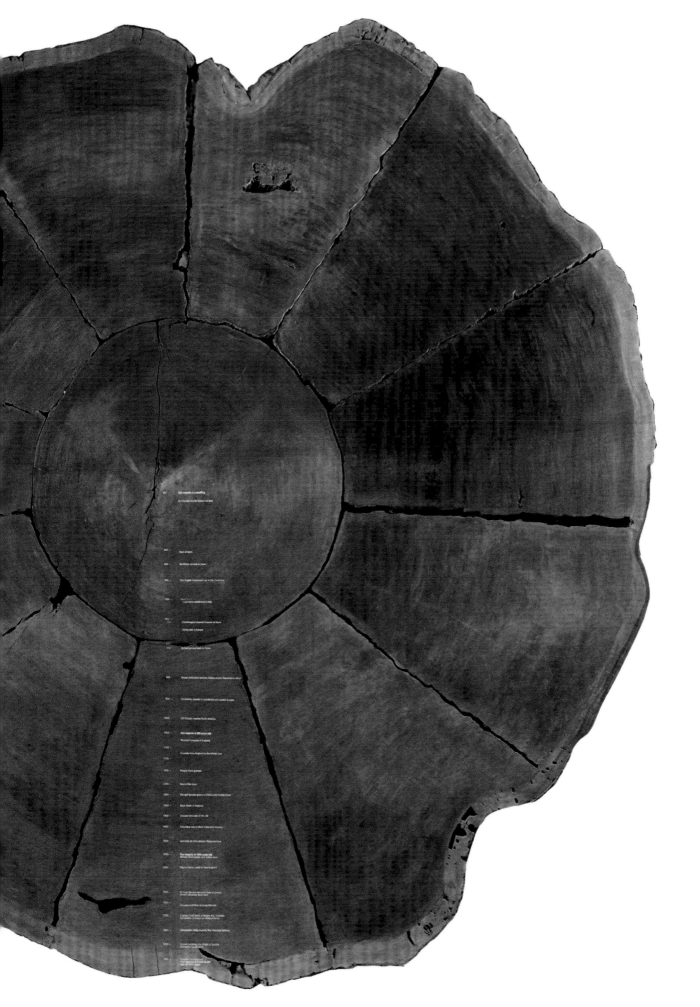

minerals

You can see the Museum as the Victorians did by visiting the tranquil *Minerals* gallery. Natural daylight pours on to long rows of low cabinets set between Waterhouse's fine terracotta columns. About ten percent of the mineral collections are on display, with examples of the Earth's main rock types, and at the end is *The Vault*, a showcase of precious minerals, gems and meteorites.

What are minerals and rocks?

A mineral is a naturally occurring substance formed through geological processes. Each has a unique chemical composition and crystal structure. Two minerals can have the same chemical elements but form quite different crystals – diamond and graphite, for example, are both crystalline carbon, but have radically different structures and properties. Rocks are made up of one or more minerals, or fragments of other rocks.

World-class collections

The remarkable collection of minerals and rocks we hold represents the Earth's geodiversity, its range of geological components. The collection is especially strong in material from Europe and former British colonies in Africa and the Far East. There are nearly 350 specimens from Sloane's original collections, including ornamental boxes and drawers of minerals once used as medicines.

Two major collections are kept as distinct entities: the Russell Collection and the Ashcroft Swiss Collection. Sir Arthur Russell was a famous collector of British minerals who left more than 12,500 items to the Museum. They include very rare specimens collected from sites no longer in existence or now inaccessible, such as the closed-down copper and tin mines of Cornwall. Frederick Noel Ashcroft's Swiss Collection is said to be the world's best-curated collection. He meticulously recorded the locality of each of his 7,000 specimens, and also kept an extensive photographic record.

What are meteorites?

Venture along the gallery to see and touch the 635-kilogramme Campo de Cielo (aka Otumpa) meteorite from Argentina, which was found in 1826. Meteorites are natural rocky and/or metallic objects that survive their fall to Earth from space. Most come from the asteroid belt, others from impacts on other planets – fragments from both the moon and Mars are in the collection. A few are rich in water, sulphur and organic (carbon-rich) compounds, materials that may have provided the chemical building blocks for life on Earth.

Meteorites give us a chance to study our solar system second hand, at a fraction of the cost of space missions. Most meteorite research focuses on exploring what happened during the formation of the solar system and of the planets.

A piece of malachite from a colourful display of ornamental stones outside the *Minerals* gallery.

4,700 meteorites and 28,000 samples from the deep ocean floor.

The Vault

A high-security room at the end of the gallery, *The Vault* showcases the most precious specimens from our mineralogy collections. With its white display cases and dazzling spotlights. It feels very different to the more traditional *Minerals* gallery. Explore the reasons for the great beauty and scientific value of the objects, and delve into their fascinating historical and cultural stories. Watch videos of experts explaining how some minerals form and why some are prized above others.

In a space where every object is a highlight, visitors can see both raw and beautifully cut diamonds, sapphires, emeralds and rubies. This is a unique chance to see objects such as the historic Latrobe nugget from the Australian gold rush, meteorites from Mars and the moon, and exceptionally fine and rare crystals from around the world.

A rainbow of colours

The Aurora Pyramid of Hope collection in *The Vault* is a world-class celebration of naturally coloured diamonds. Unlike the more familiar white diamonds, these 296 stones, together weighing 267 carats, represent every colour of the spectrum, from red and yellow to purple and orange. The colour of diamond is caused by minute amounts of trace elements or structural defects that affect the way light is reflected and absorbed. You can see this selection under fluorescent light, which causes many of the stones to change colour and glow. Coloured diamonds are very rare and highly prized, in particular the red, pink, blue, green and gold stones.

Crushed purple fluorite was used as a natural pigment in certain paintings between c. 1450 and 1520.

fossil marine reptiles

Scan the walls of this long light-filled gallery and you'll find a flourish of remarkable specimens, including the fossilised remains of huge marine reptiles. These are the fish-like ichthyosaurs, paddle-limbed plesiosaurs and shorter-necked pliosaurs, mosasaurs and marine crocodiles – all powerful predators. Although now preserved on our walls, they lived during the time dinosaurs dominated the land.

Fossil hunters

Twenty-six of the specimens on display were sold to the British Museum in 1834 by a flamboyant fossil collector called Thomas Hawkins (1810–1889), who promoted his finds as fabulous sea monsters. The largest, his 'great sea dragon', is an enormous ichthyosaur called *Temnodontosaurus platyodon*, which Hawkins bought from another famous collector, Mary Anning.

Mary Anning (1799–1847) found her first ichthyosaur at the age of 11, in the cliffs along the Dorset coast in England where she lived. The counties of Dorset and Somerset are especially rich in marine fossils, because the right-aged sediments – formed from ancient seabeds – are exposed in quarries and cliffs. It was Anning who discovered the first almost complete ichthyosaur, plesiosaur and pterosaur fossils ever found in Britain. She built a thriving business selling fossils, and her reputation as a collector and expert grew. Anning was consulted by many of the leading scientists of the day, such as William Buckland (1784–1856), the first man to give a name to a dinosaur – *Megalosaurus*. Some of Anning's correspondence is kept in our Archives.

Mary Anning inspired the tongue-twister 'She sells seashells on the sea-shore'.

Fish lizards

The ichthyosaurs, meaning fish lizards, were the dolphins of their day, swift and deadly hunters with large eyes and long, sharp-toothed jaws. Like dolphins, they gave birth to live young in the water. We know this from fossils that show embryos in the body of adults. One fossil appears to capture the moment of birth itself, the baby just expelled from its mother's body.

The long-snouted ichthyosaur, *Leptopterygius tenuirostris*, swam in the seas over 200 million years ago.

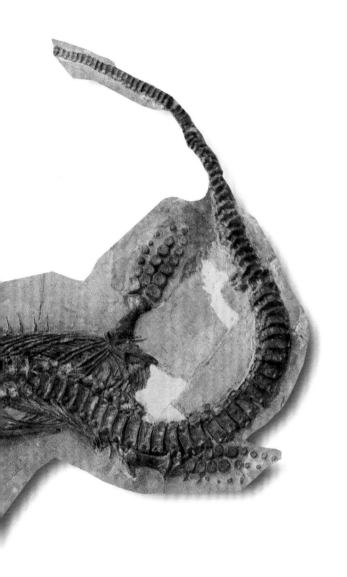

Giant sloth

One of the most photographed specimens in this gallery isn't a marine reptile at all. Instead it is a four-metre-high replica skeleton of the ground sloth *Megatherium*. This land mammal was one of several gigantic plant-eaters that lived in South America between 100,000 and 11,000 years ago, a time when the north was gripped in a series of ice ages. Voyaging scientists such as Charles Darwin brought their curious bones back to Europe. Richard Owen described and named many of them, including *Megatherium* and *Glyptodon*, the tank-like giant armadillo, which you can see in the Hintze Hall.

> Behold the Great Sea-Dragon, the Emperor of Past Worlds, maleficent, terrible, direct, and sublime.

Thomas Hawkins, Sea Dragons, 1860

creepy crawlies

A larger-than-life model of a stag beetle greets you at the entrance to the *Creepy Crawlies* gallery, a striking reminder of life at a very different scale from our own. This gallery is devoted to the arthropods – from flying and crawling insects and spiders, to scuttling crabs and their relatives. As well as models and specimens, there are films, interactives, and a live, bustling colony of leafcutter ants from Trinidad.

Diversity

The diversity of arthropods is hard to capture: behind the scenes, we hold more than 30 million insect specimens alone, belonging to about 600,000 species. And they represent only a fraction of the species that may exist. Arthropods are found in every habitat, from spiders on Everest to crabs crawling over sulphurous deep-sea vents and parasitic lice at home in our hair. They come in a bewildering variety of shapes and sizes, fantastic colours and patterns. Many are armed with impressive weapons, while others create amazing architecture such as the webs of spiders.

Nature's knights

All adult arthropods have a hard external skeleton, which performs the same function as a suit of armour. The word arthropod means jointed limb, and the number of limbs is an easy guide to the different groups: insects have six legs; spiders, scorpions and mites have eight, while crustaceans (crabs and their relatives) have 10. Centipedes have between 30 and 100 and the millipedes up to 400 (never 1,000).

Friends and foes

Arthropods play an important part in our lives. Some pollinate our food crops and play a big role in soil fertility, while others damage them and carry diseases. Museum scientists are working all over the world to understand their impact on us – and our impact on them. We monitor the diversity of insects and other arthropods in soil and leaf litter in the UK and around the world, and we assess their ecological role. In South America and other parts of the tropics, we are searching for new species of parasitoid wasps that can act as natural control agents of many pest insects. In China, we study the impact of overgrazing on pollinating bumblebees.

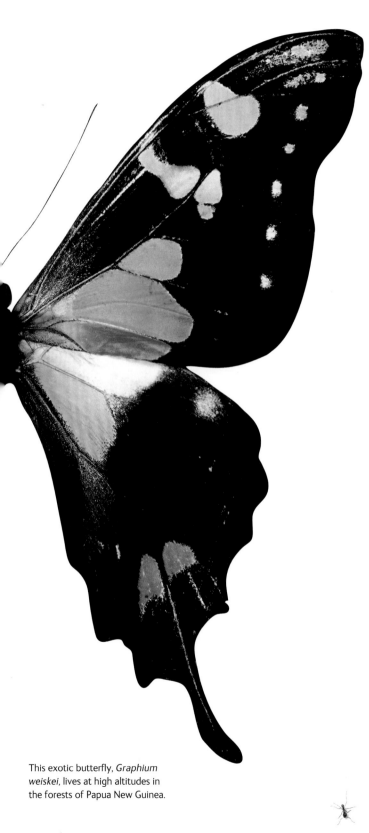

This exotic butterfly, *Graphium weiskei*, lives at high altitudes in the forests of Papua New Guinea.

A jumping flea accelerates 50 times faster than a space shuttle.

House guests

From fleas to flour beetles, arthropods make their homes in ours. Most are harmless, a few helpful, but some can carry disease, or chew through clothing, furniture and roof timbers. At the Museum, too, we have to be on constant alert. The collections we look after are a potential paradise for the long-haired larvae of 'museum' beetles, which belong to the same group as the common carpet beetle found in many houses. They feed on natural fibres such as silk, wool, fur, leather and any dried animal remains. When newly hatched, they can crawl through minute cracks in wooden cabinets, and so we've converted to sealed metal ones.

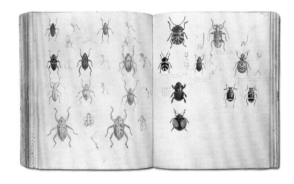

Safety in disguise

The collection of Henry Walter Bates (1825–1892) is prized. He spent 11 years in the Amazon, collected over 14,000 specimens, and identified 8,000 new species. He made detailed notes of everything he collected, and illustrated many of them (above). Bates noticed that many harmless insects copied the appearance of poisonous or distasteful species. This form of protective mimicry is now known as Batesian mimicry.

ecology

A dramatic glass canyon leads along the central aisle of the *Ecology* gallery as it wraps around the original terracotta columns. Criss-crossing glass bridges divide the space into discrete exhibits which bring to life basic ideas in ecology – the study of the web of connections that link living things and their environment. Other areas explore the impact of our own species on the natural world, and ask how we can all get involved in reducing and repairing the damage that humans are causing.

Inside the leaf factory you'll discover how different parts of the leaf use the sun to convert carbon dioxide and water into oxygen in the process of photosynthesis.

Water cycles, energy flows

Life on Earth depends on a constant flow of water and nutrients, and of energy from the sun. The endless cycle of water through air, bodies of water, rock and the living world is captured dramatically on film in a giant globe. Enter the heart of a leaf and stand among the cells that trap the sun's energy for food, and make it available to other living things. This is the beginning of the food webs that connect us all. Energy and nutrients flow from one organism to another, between living and non-living systems. Nothing is wasted. Waste from one creature, and eventually its body, is broken down and returned to the cycle.

Protecting diversity

The Museum plays a key role in gathering information about our natural heritage and how it's changing. Many British species are in decline, from songbirds and snakes to insects vital to agriculture. Bees, for example, are important pollinators, but populations of some species are falling. We need to know why in order to protect and build their numbers. Climate change may be a factor, but vanishing wildflower meadows and gardens kept too tidy could also be a cause.

Reduce, re-use, recycle

Human beings are as much a part of the natural world as any other living thing. We have been incredibly successful in exploiting nature's resources, but this comes at a high price. We pollute, degrade and destroy natural habitats, and displace, isolate and drive other species to extinction. But what we do to the planet will increasingly affect us.

The challenge is now to work with, not against, nature, taking less and giving more. Everyone can do something positive, whether it's reducing energy and water use, sorting rubbish or reducing packaging. We can grow food, work on a local nature reserve or put up a bat box, walk rather than drive. And we can make space for nature in our cities and towns – as the Wildlife Garden at the Museum shows (see page 16).

> ‘ Nature is not a place to visit, it is home. ’
>
> *Gary Snyder, American poet*

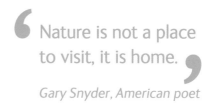

birds

Immerse yourself in the world of birds in this gallery, where you'll find a family of flightless ostriches, flamboyant peacocks and exotic hummingbirds, blackbirds that are white and the largest eggs ever laid. There are birds with tube-like beaks to suck nectar from deep flowers, blunt nut-cracking beaks and sharp hooked beaks to tear at flesh. There are extinct species and others on the verge of extinction, and a cast of one of the most important fossils in the Museum, *Archaeopteryx*. About 150 million years old, it's the oldest bird yet found (see page 34).

What is a bird?

Birds are warm-blooded vertebrates that lay hard-shelled eggs and have feathers. Their forelimbs are modified as wings and most can fly, but some have lost the ability to do so and some, like the penguins, 'fly' through water rather than air.

The bird egg is a perfectly packaged home for the developing chick, containing all the food it will need. A tough membrane inside the shell allows air in and out. The largest egg in the world was laid by the now extinct elephant bird of Madagascar. It's bigger than any dinosaur egg yet discovered. The smallest known egg is laid by the vervain hummingbird.

Gone but not forgotten

Dodos are more famous for dying out than for anything they did in life. These large flightless birds, closely related to pigeons, were discovered on the Indian Ocean island of Mauritius by Europeans in 1598, and were probably wiped out by the late 1660s. They had no defence against the hunters and the animals brought by them to the island – especially pigs, rats and monkeys, which attacked their nests.

This classic reconstruction of the dodo is now considered to be inaccurate.

Remarkably few remains of dodos exist, but new fossil material including rare items, such as a dodo beak and young dodos, has recently been discovered by a Dutch-Mauritian research team. It is hoped that this new evidence will reveal what life was like for the dodo before humans arrived, and will also help us to understand more about extinction events on Mauritius and other oceanic islands.

Flights of fancy

This showcase crammed with hummingbirds is a highlight for many visitors, and dates from the early 1800s. The tiny brightly coloured hummingbirds astonished people then, and a huge trade grew in their skins. Prolonged exposure to light has faded most of the birds to brown, but some feathering still flashes with iridescent colour.

Victorian displays

The gallery boasts two large Victorian triangular wooden cases. One is a meticulous arrangement of bird anatomy, with pinned beaks, bodies, heads and wings. The other is a mix of albino birds, plus a startling display of eggs, from the enormous 400-kilogramme elephant bird egg to the tiny egg of a hummingbird, no bigger than a little fingernail. The Museum had 159 such cases but sadly most were destroyed in air raids during the Second World War.

There are more than 350 species of parrot and one-quarter of them are at a high risk of extinction.

! The goldcrest lays the smallest egg of any British bird.

dinosaurs

For many, the Natural History Museum is synonymous with dinosaurs, and so *Dinosaurs* is one of our most popular galleries. This dark, exciting space, spanned by a skeletal steel bridge, explores the science of these fantastic creatures, from horned *Triceratops* to bonyheaded *Pachycephalosaurus*, and perhaps the most famous of all, a moving *Tyrannosaurus rex*.

What is a dinosaur?

Dinosaurs were a group of ancient land reptiles, which walked with straight legs tucked under them rather than sprawling like lizards. Over 160 million years, between 230 and 65 million years ago, they evolved into an astonishing array of forms. To date more than 800 species have been discovered from sites all over the world: long-necked plant-eaters, powerful predators and smaller, swifter pack hunters. The largest creatures ever to live on land were dinosaurs, but some were no bigger than a pigeon.

Bringing dinosaurs to life

Dinosaurs have captured people's imagination since the first monstrous fossils were discovered. But what were they really like? Was *T. rex* a terrifying predator, or a scavenger, too slow and cumbersome to hunt down its own dinner? In the exhibition you can find out what scientists can learn from bones, skulls and teeth, tracks and even droppings. Joints can show how they moved; an impression in mud gives a clue to skin patterning, head structures hint at sounds they could have made and a nest of eggs suggest how they looked after their young. All these clues put together help to bring extinct dinosaurs back to life.

The fast-moving *Velociraptor* was a hunter with powerful claws and needle-sharp teeth. It had short fine feathers on its torso and larger ones on its arms, tail and head.

Why did they die out?

With the exception of their direct descendants, the birds, dinosaurs became extinct about 65 million years ago. And arguments continue as to why. There is evidence of a massive meteorite striking Earth, but a single sudden catastrophe is unlikely to have caused such wholesale extinction. Sea levels were falling and at the same time intense volcanic eruptions were throwing out poison gases and darkening the skies. The combined effect may have been enough to finish the dinosaurs off.

Tooth and claw

The Museum has one of the finest collections of dinosaur material in the world, including some of the earliest dinosaur fossils ever described. These are the strange iguana-like teeth collected by Mary and Gideon Mantell in 1822, and the Maidstone slab, a partial skeleton bought for Mantell by his friends in 1834. He originally named both sets of remains *Iguanodon*, but the animal in the Maidstone slab is now called *Mantellisaurus* in his honour.

In 1983, Museum scientists unearthed one of the most complete skeletons of a meat-eating dinosaur found in Europe that century. It was later named *Baryonyx walkeri* after William Walker, an amateur fossil hunter who found its claw. Its unusually long skull was armed with teeth well-suited to catching and gripping fish, and it may have used its great hand claw to hook fish out of the water.

Are there dinosaurs today?

When Richard Owen persuaded the Museum to buy a curious feathered fossil in 1862, he could not have predicted just how precious it would turn out to be. The *Archaeopteryx* remains one of only 10 fossils of this unique, 150-million-year-old bird with reptile-like features. Over the next century, other feathered fossils have emerged, especially from China. Some were clearly fast-running dinosaurs with a feathery covering, from which most scientists now agree birds evolved.

T. rex had a bone-crushing bite, three times more powerful than the bite of a lion.

mammals

Wander through the *Mammals* gallery and you will find it's in two parts, very different in look and feel. The first is a classic display of specimens in glass cases, where a lion and a panda stare out as you walk by. The second is a more theatrical display of large beasts, with the massive blue whale as the centrepiece. It easily dwarfs the nearby elephant, giraffe and rhino.

What is a mammal?

The basic definition of a mammal is a four-limbed, warm-blooded creature with fur or hair, which gives birth to live young and suckles them with milk. However, there are exceptions that have evolved to fit a wide range of niches. The platypus still lays eggs, dolphins have no fur and bats have wings instead of front legs. But they all share the same basic body plan and physiology.

The first mammals evolved 220 million years ago, but remained small and insignificant during the reign of the giant dinosaurs. The many forms we know today are relatively recent in Earth history. Displays around the whale show the diversity of both living and extinct mammals, from portly wide-mouthed hippos to delicate antelopes. The upper balcony is teeming with exhibits that explore the behaviour and intelligence of whales and dolphins, and introduce the seals, sea lions and seacows, said to be the origin of the mermaid myth.

Recent genetic studies have shown that polar bears are in fact brown bears that became isolated in a northern coastal refuge.

Blue giant

The blue whale model is a visitor favourite. Almost 30 metres long, it was constructed on site in the gallery in 1938 and modelled on beached whales, without the benefit of modern underwater photography. We now know the whale is usually much sleeker in life and the flexible throat is fully extended only when feeding. The blue whale is the largest animal to ever live. It has a heart the size of a small family car, with arteries like drainpipes.

Whale strandings

Whales and dolphins are regularly stranded along our shores. In 1913 the Crown's right to claim these Fishes Royal was transferred to the Museum. Since then we have been central to the monitoring of strandings in the United Kingdom. More than 12,000 have been recorded, including some species new to British waters. The Natural History Museum plays an important role in the collaborative UK Cetacean Strandings Investigation Programme, which is a vital part of nationwide research into the status of whale and dolphin populations around the British Isles. Studies of strandings help us to understand their diversity, distribution and any threats to their survival from pollution, fishing or disease. The Museum currently processes reports of more than 800 strandings per year.

Stranded in central London

In January 2006, a disoriented northern bottlenose whale swam up London's River Thames, far from its North Atlantic home. Sadly, rescue attempts failed and after pathologists carried out a post-mortem its body was examined by Museum staff. DNA samples were taken and its skeleton became part of our scientific collection. Most years two to five bottlenose whales strand on our coasts, and we hold 34 other examples of this species. The more material we have, the more we can learn about their biology, genetics and population changes over time.

Manatees
Sirenians

Rhinos, tapirs, horses

Fake horn

Elephant past and present

A series of specimens, skeletons and models tell the 40-million-year story of elephant evolution, from strange little barrel-bodied *Moeritherium*, with only the hint of a trunk, to the spectacular woolly mammoth. This magnificent creature was hunted by early humans, possibly to extinction. Its relatives are equally vulnerable today. A pair of trophy tusks, the largest in the world, stand close to a bull African elephant that was shot to order many years ago – a moving reminder of the threat posed by humans. Today, elephants, rhinos, hippos and many other species are protected, but poaching continues. Habitat loss and the encroachment of human populations threaten the larger, slower-breeding mammal species most.

! African elephants are the largest of Earth's land mammals.

A hippo's tusks can grow to 60 cm or as long as your arm.

images of nature

Before the arrival of photography and film, scientists depended on artists to produce detailed illustrations. The best were acclaimed for the accuracy of their work, and were highly sought-after. Contemporary scientists still illustrate their own work, but drawing now sits alongside a suite of technological methods for recording nature, from scanning electron microscopes to satellites.

In the gallery you can explore highlights from the world-famous collection of natural history artworks held in the Museum. Irreplaceable historic material and modern works sit beside images created by our scientists, imaging specialists and photographers. Beautiful and intriguing, these artworks and images are also an important visual record of the natural world that spans more than 350 years.

Period and contemporary images sit side-by-side. A haunting chalk drawing of a giant tortoise by Bryan Kneale from 1986 hangs on the same walls as a seventeenth-century oil painting of a dodo, attributed to the Flemish artist Roelandt Savery. The Savery painting hangs next to a modern interpretation of the dodo in acrylic by artist and Museum scientist Dr Julian Pender Hume. One section changes each year, to cover more topics and some paintings are replaced periodically to limit light damage.

Six kiosks let you watch videos or zoom in and examine certain images. For the truly inspired, there are cards and pencils on hand for you to draw your favourite Museum specimen.

The life size picture of a giant tortoise skeleton expertly displays the specimen's main features.

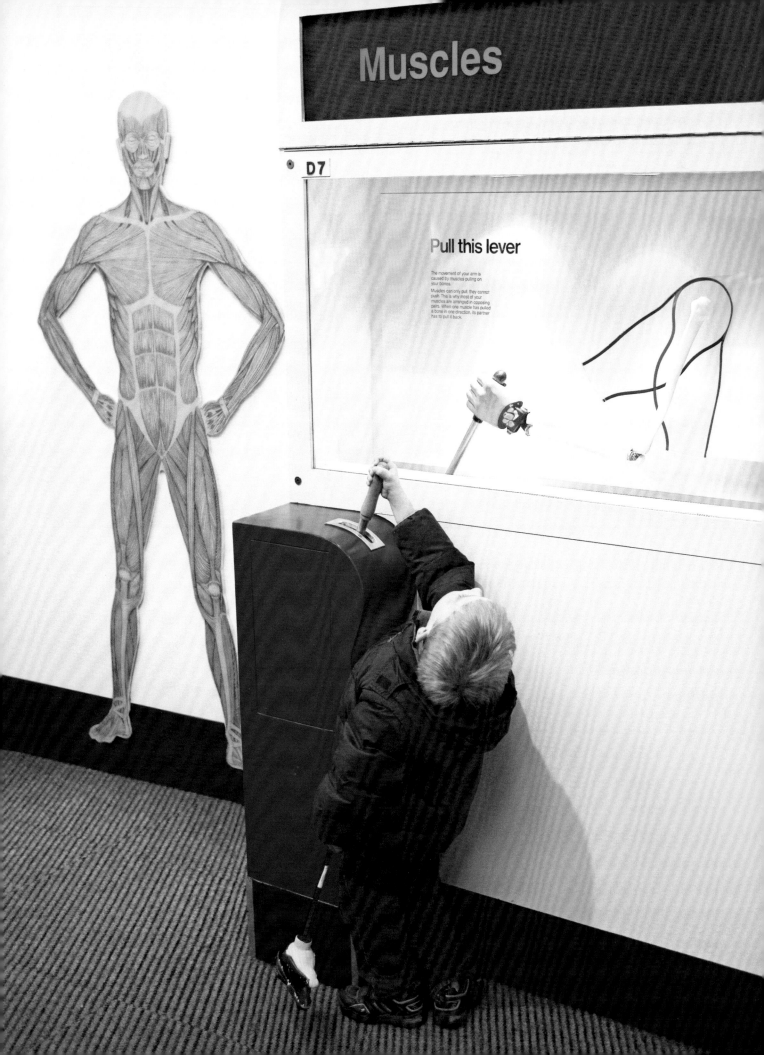

Muscles

D7

Pull this lever

The movement of your arm is caused by muscles pulling on your bones.

Muscles can only pull, they cannot push. This is why most of your muscles are arranged in opposing pairs. When one muscle has pulled a bone in one direction, its partner has to pull it back.

human biology

Discover yourself in this exhibition, where you're both the subject and the object. Apart from a brain and spinal cord, there are no specimens. Instead, interactive exhibits, models and films let you uncover how you began, how you developed in the womb, the way you move, how you learned to think – and talk – and what skills of perception and memory you now have.

Beginnings

The exhibition begins the same way you did, as a cell, the body's basic building block. Watch on film the extraordinary path we took from a single egg cell fertilised by a sperm to a newborn. It shows how the body's complex layers, tissues and organs gradually take shape. Beyond, a dark chamber offers a return to the womb to listen to the rhythmic sounds of a mother's heart, in the company of a giant seven-month-old model foetus.

Life-long learning

Human beings are born remarkably helpless, our bodies uncoordinated and weak, our brains not yet fully formed. It takes nearly two decades of growing and learning for us to reach adulthood. All that time, we are learning to make sense of the world and other people's behaviour, acquiring physical and mental skills, and how to put our thoughts into words and pictures. Naturally curious creatures, we never stop learning.

Learning and remembering are the two main processes of memory.

In control

The brain is a complex, highly organised mass of one billion nerve cells. It controls almost everything we do, from breathing, eating and walking to solving sums and writing poetry. But some emergency actions, called reflexes, are controlled at the level of the spinal cord, the long tube of nerves that runs down from it. If you accidentally touch something hot, you withdraw your hand before your brain even registers the sensation.

! There are as many red blood cells in a drop of your blood as there are people using London buses every day.

Seeing what isn't there

For all our extraordinary skills, our brains can play tricks on us, so we see things that are not there, or remember things that didn't actually happen. That's because our brains make sense of the world by filling in gaps and making assumptions based on what we have learned and remember. We find it much more difficult to remember a list of random numbers than a sequence, or of random words rather than a grammatical sentence, even if the sentence is nonsense. And we often 'remember' what we expect to have happened rather than what actually happened, which is why we make poor witnesses.

marine invertebrates

The cases lining this gallery are filled with enchanting shells, corals and other specimens. These are the marine invertebrates, creatures without a backbone, that inhabit the oceans, covering two-thirds of the planet's surface. Many are startlingly beautiful, and the temptation throughout history to collect them now threatens many with extinction.

Exotic diversity

Marine invertebrates range from the gigantic to microscopic creatures too tiny to put on display. There are sponges, corals and worms, sea urchins, squid and octopus, hard-shelled molluscs and crustaceans. Curious creatures include colonial animals called bryozoans that turn cartwheels across the seabed on their spines, shellfish that gather other shells into their own. There are sea stars with a basketful of arms, and parasitic worms that wind their way round the guts of marine fish.

Cone shells are from tropical reefs. Some kinds have a deadly sting.

Fragile beauty

One of the most beautiful specimens on display is a group of sponges called Venus' flower baskets, arranged in a Victorian glass dome. In fact, what you see are only their bleached  'skeletons', delicate lattices of microscopic six-armed silica spicules. Many species of sponge are identified by the shape of their spicules, which survive far better than soft parts. Behind the scenes, we look after 60 percent of the world's type specimens of sponges, those precious individuals used to define each species.

Corals and conservation

Coral reefs are very tough – the devastating 2004 tsunami in Asia could not shake them. But they are very vulnerable to pollution, sea warming and the effects of tourism. However, the worst damage is done through over-harvesting for sale. International treaties ban trade in endangered corals, but the business is lucrative and smuggling continues. When police and customs intercept large hauls of coral destined for the commercial market they bring them here for identification. Our scientists use the reference collections to check if any are endangered.

This a coral sea fan, *Gorgonia flabellum*, found in the shallow waters of the Caribbean. It can grow to more than 1.5 metres tall and wide.

 We look after about 23 million marine invertebrate specimens such as vampire squid and rare corals.

fishes, amphibians and reptiles

Nestled behind the corridor leading from the Central Café is the world of the lower vertebrates: the fish, amphibians and reptiles. From hairy frogs and man-eating crocodiles to fish that make their own light, these are the most ancient vertebrates on Earth, and some of the most endangered.

Ancient survivors

This group illustrates life's transition, over hundreds of millions of years, from a watery existence to life on land. Considered by some to be not as charismatic as their warm-blooded relatives, they are nevertheless highly successful survivors from long before mammals and birds emerged.

The exhibits can only give a taste of their incredible diversity, but among them are many world-record holders, from the model of a 15-metre-long whale shark to West Africa's goliath frog, which can grow as big as a house cat. The largest lizard on Earth, the dangerous Komodo dragon, dominates its case, while a huge crocodile – displayed with some of the contents of its last meal – sits above an alligator.

The curiosities

Among these attention-grabbers are some surprises, such as the delicate bones of a flatfish, like the remains of a fish supper. There's a tortoise skeleton split in two showing how its backbone and ribs fuse to form the protective shell. See the rhythmic repetition of ribs along a python's skeleton and the small snake swallowing an egg whole, a salamander that never grows up, and a tadpole three times larger than the frog into which it grows.

 There are almost as many fish species alive today as all the birds, reptiles, amphibians and mammals combined.

Amphibian – double life

Fish, with hardly an exception, are water-bound, while most reptiles can live their whole lives as air-breathers on land. But amphibians lead a double life, as anyone with a garden pond will know. Frogs, toads and newts go through a quite astonishing transformation during their life cycle, from water-living tadpoles to air-breathing adults. Some species show strange variations on this theme – the eggs can be carried in pockets on the mother's back, brooded by the male in its vocal sac or, as with the midwife toad, wrapped round the male's hind legs.

Secrets from the deep

The display on deep-sea fish shows just how curious life can get. This vast region, 2,000–5,000 metres below the surface, is one of the least explored areas on our planet. Many strange creatures exist here that are quite unlike anything found nearer the surface. There are fish that never see the light of day, so make their own. Some hunt with lures on inbuilt 'fishing rods', and others swallow meals as big as themselves. Here at the Museum we look after one of the largest and most important collections of deep-sea creatures in the world. They play a vital role in helping us to map the sea's diversity.

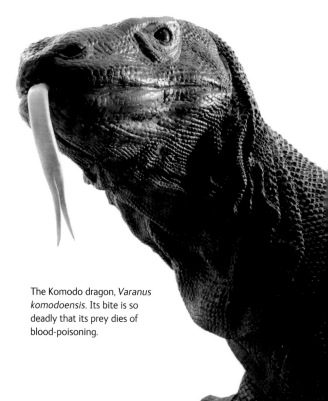

The Komodo dragon, *Varanus komodoensis*. Its bite is so deadly that its prey dies of blood-poisoning.

lasting impressions

This light and airy gallery connects the main Waterhouse building with the more modern galleries of the 1930s that explore Earth's processes. Specimens encircle the room, many of which can be touched, and each carrying a record of its own history. They may capture a moment in time or a lifetime's growth, the growth happening at very different paces. A patch of lichen on a rock may grow no more than a millimetre in 50 years. A bamboo might extend more than 20 metres in a single two-month growing season.

Weekly timetable

Sunday stone – a delicate slice of rock, like a musical score in black and cream. This rock records the working rhythm of a coalmine in the 1880s, as layers of white barium sulphate crystals settled in a water pipe. Each dark line represents a day's coal dust washed out of the mine. Sundays and public holidays are marked by a wider white stripe when the mine was closed.

A moment in time

Some specimens record a single event. A thin red line running through a coral captures the sudden pollution of its environment with iron. Ripples in sand, frozen into rock, are marked with what are possibly the footprints of a primitive reptile that walked across a sandy beach, 230 million years ago.

A record of growth

Many specimens show growth rings, marking cycles of growth over months and years. In a fossil tree trunk they have turned to rock as the wood has been replaced by minerals. There are also growth patterns in goat horns and seashells. A beautiful fossil of an ammonite, an extinct relative of the octopus and squid, illustrates how it grew by adding chambers to its coiled shell. After death, the chambers became mineralised and filled with crystals.

Bamboo is the fastest growing plant in the world.

earth hall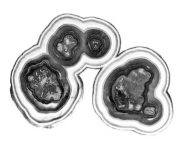

As you enter the Earth Hall from Exhibition Road, you come face-to-face with a *Stegosaurus*. This specimen was found in Wyoming, USA with more than 90 percent of its bones intact, making it the most complete *Stegosaurus* fossil skeleton ever found. High above it, a huge metallic globe through which an escalator rises, dominates the atrium. The globe almost touches the high slate walls, which are etched with images of the planets and stars. The atrium is the starting point for exhibitions exploring our planet, the processes that shape and change it and the many mineral treasures it produces. The main exhibitions are upstairs but along each wall on the ground floor is a series of portals, which each hold geological wonders.

Stegosaurus lived around 150 million years ago. A slow-moving plant-eater, it would have used its four vicious 38-centimetre-long tail spikes as protection against other dinosaur predators. This *Stegosaurus* was discovered in 2003 and was a young adult when it died.

Windows of exploration

Some of the portals contain minerals that are beautiful. The flourite and willemite specimens glow, displayed under UV light. There is rainbow-coloured opal and glittering fool's gold – also known as pyrite – and a sculpted figure in jade. Other portals hold specimens that have historical importance, such as a piece of Moon rock from the *Apollo 16* mission. A trio of salt-petre (potassium nitrate) sulphur and charcoal have explosive results – they form gunpowder when combined. There is a fossil of the extinct plant that drove the industrial revolution, a lepidodendron tree, one of the main components of the fossil fuel coal. Other fossils include the shell of an extinct mollusc said to be the toenail of a devil, and a perfectly preserved stingray from 50 million years ago.

Our universe is 15,000 million years old, our solar system 4,567 million years old and Earth was formed 4,540 million years ago.

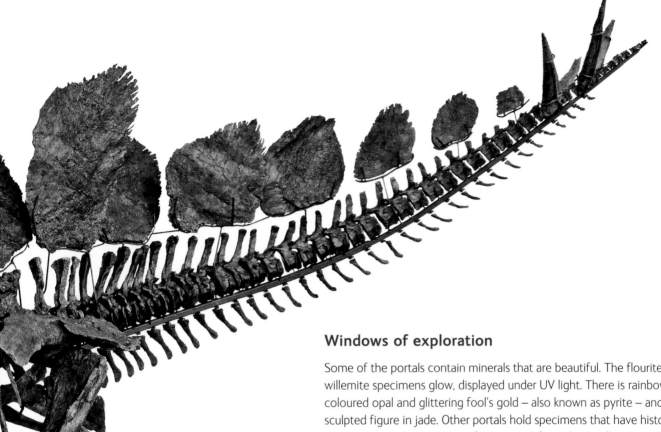

Azurite (left), malachite (right) and chalcotrichite (top) are all copper minerals. Ground malachite and azurite were used as pigments to colour paint.

volcanoes and earthquakes

The story begins at the top of a great escalator that rides through a metallic globe. An impressive sweep of rocks leads to *Volcanoes and Earthquakes*. This exhibition explores the powerful forces at work deep within Earth that shape its surface, and how scientists learn about this hidden world. Volcanoes and earthquakes are the surface evidence of these forces. Volcanoes cause devastation when they erupt, as the Earth's surface is thrown into convulsions and explosive eruptions fire molten rock and ash high into the air, while lava flows and pyroclastic flows can wipe out everything in their path. Earthquakes wreak destruction directly or by causing tsunami or landslides.

Touch real rocks from volcanoes across the world – specimens from the Giant's Causeway in Northern Ireland and lava from Indonesia. Learn how water heated by underground magma can transport metals and other elements in solution and deposit them as minerals in rocks nearer the surface. See what volcanologists wear to get close to active volcanoes but remain protected from temperatures of up to 900 degrees Celsius and dangerous volcanic ashes.

The human cost

The exhibition contains stark reminders of the human cost of the planet's violent motion. You can see models of a man and dog entombed in ash from the eruption of Mount Vesuvius, Italy, on the morning of 24 August, AD 79. An earthquake simulator uses real footage to tell the story of the 1995 earthquake in Kobe, Japan, which caused massive damage and loss of life.

Since then, there has been even greater destruction. In December 2004, an earthquake deep below the Indian Ocean unleashed a tsunami that killed over 200,000 people and wrecked coastlines from Sumatra to India. In October 2005, a violent earthquake in Kashmir took many thousands of lives. In March 2011, Japan's most powerful earthquake since records began struck the northeast coast, triggering a massive tsunami which then led to a nuclear crisis and huge leaks of radiation.

Experience what it feels like to be in a small earthquake.

Deep forces

Devastating as they are, volcanoes and earthquakes are only minor surface signs of far greater forces at work deep below, forces so massive that whole continents are moved across the planet's surface, as part of giant tectonic plates. These plates are in constant, slow motion. At their margins, new plate forms or sinks slowly back into the depths. It is along these lines of weakness that most volcanoes and earthquakes occur. The drifting plates are driven by giant currents of rock that flow through the Earth's mantle, the 2,900-kilometre zone between the plate and the molten outer core. Over geological time their movement throws up mountains and creates new oceans.

Deep-sea ridges

Deep-sea exploration in the 1960s revealed vast mountain ranges beneath the oceans, which mark the plate boundaries where new plates are created. There, hot mineral-laden water escapes from chimney-like vents called hydrothermal vents. An extraordinary range of life thrives in this dark hostile environment, including giant tubeworms, clams and crustaceans.

Discovery of this world helped our Museum geologists and their Russian colleagues to understand some puzzling fossil layers they had found in the Ural Mountains of central Russia when searching for new mineral deposits. They realised that they were looking at an ancient deep-sea floor, about 370 million years old.

! Plates are slowly but constantly being created and destroyed, at the same speed your fingernails grow.

Giant tubeworms, two metres long, can take 200 years to reach this size.

restless surface

Watery sediments begin to turn to rock as they are compacted.

The sounds of wind and rain fill the darkly lit opening space of this gallery, evoking the power of wind and water to transform the surface of the land, as surely as volcanoes and earthquakes do. Change may come suddenly, with a violent landslide or raging storm, or slowly, drip by drip, over millions of years. Ours is a restless planet, and change is part of its nature.

Wind, water, ice and gravity sculpt the landscape, wearing down mountains and carving out deep ravines. Their destructive power is matched only by their power to build, as they carry millions of tonnes of debris that will in time settle and cement to form new rocks and new landscapes.

Reading the rocks

A host of specimens to touch show that rocks hold their own story within them – we only have to learn how to read them. The smooth texture of a rounded pebble tells of its long journey along a river, tumbling and rolling in water, while a jagged fragment may have been trapped in the ice of a flowing glacier, with no opportunity to rub against its companions. The stripes of a lake bed sediment show the annual rhythm of debris flushed into the lake with spring floods.

Water sculpture

Water is the greatest shaper of the world's landscapes. It wears away at the surface both chemically and physically. As ice it can crack open boulders and grind out deep valleys. As flowing water it can eat away caves and build up towering stalagmites. It can sweep up fragments of rock and carry them hundreds of kilometres, then deposit them in vast sandbanks and river deltas.

Life into rock

Life is also part of the restless process of change. Limestone hills and chalk cliffs are formed from the remains of living things. Over the millennia, billions of skeletons of tiny marine creatures sank to the bottom of the sea, building layers hundreds of metres deep. In time, these were compressed and cemented together, and gradually land movements and changing sea levels exposed them at the surface.

These carbon-rich rocks are part of the planet's carbon cycle, which circulates carbon between living and non-living worlds, and between the surface and deep mantle.

A whole history in a single boulder

This one rock, with its complex fragments of layered pink crystals among grey debris, tells of a long cycle of change. First, a cave formed as groundwater eroded the rock, then minerals grew in brightly coloured layers on its roof and walls. An earthquake caused the roof to collapse, and water crept between the broken debris, depositing new mineral crystals.

from the beginning

This dramatic gallery has the daunting task of telling the 4,540 million-year-old history of Earth, and how life emerged and then diversified here, shaped by endless cycles of geological change. It's a turbulent history of floating and colliding continents, climate change, mass extinctions and exploding variety. A stunning array of fossils, some dating back more than 500 million years, stretches along a timeline that runs the length of the gallery. Every step takes you 25 million years along the path to the present.

The 'big bang'

The story begins with the origins of the universe itself. Most scientists believe about 15,000 million years ago, all matter – and time – came into being in the 'big bang', when a tiny fireball of infinite density and heat exploded, and expanded, perhaps even faster than the speed of light. Matter gradually clumped together to form galaxies and stars. Our own galaxy evolved about 10,000 million years ago, our solar system formed about 4,567 million years ago. Earth slowly took its present shape.

Rocks containing what many regard as the oldest known fossils (c. 3,500 million years old) are in the Museum collection.

Life begins

The earliest signs of single-celled life come from sedimentary rocks 4,000 million years old, but more complex forms did not emerge until about 550 million years ago. It seems there was then an explosion of life, with many bizarre creatures evolving that bear no resemblance to anything living today, and others that are still remarkably familiar in form. The 500-million-year-old *Anomalocaris* – a marine predator – was pieced together from fossilised remains, each of which was originally thought to be a separate animal. We have found 570-million-year-old fossils of jellyfish that look very like they do today.

Life on land

Plants and animals populated the dry land between about 470 and 395 million years ago. Invertebrates, such as crawling insects and giant centipedes, were the first to emerge, and four-legged vertebrates, such as slow-moving amphibians, followed quickly. There were sprawling amphibians and massive reptiles such as the bulky *Bradysaurus* – its limbs more like crudely hewn boulders – and eventually, the dinosaurs.

The delicate flower of *Porana oeningensis* is about 20 million years old.

BIG BANG

SOLAR SYSTEM BORN
EARTH FORMS
MOON FORMS

OLDEST ROCKS

FIRST RIVERS, LAKES & SEAS

15000   13500   5000   4567 4540 4533   4030   3850

MILLION YEARS AGO

Mass extinctions

The fossil record appears to show that life on Earth has gone through cycles of extinction, when whole groups disappear from the fossil record, and other groups then diversify to take their place. The best known of these is the event that caused the extinction of the non-avian dinosaurs. But there have been five such cycles. Our species may be causing a sixth.

Brief past, what future?

The final section of the exhibition changes pace with the arrival of human beings – now every metre in the space measures out 500,000 years. Our species emerged against the backdrop of the great cycles of freezing and warming we call the ice ages. Somehow, we learned to survive and prosper. Many of the great beasts that evolved alongside us during these periods are extinct, some possibly at our hands. Today, our success continues to threaten the survival of the creatures with which we share our environment.

Mapping the past

Being able to date rock formations is vital in geological research. Among the treasures we care for are maps made by William 'Strata' Smith (1769–1839). Sometimes known as the father of English geology, he produced the first large-scale geological map to be published in the world. Smith was a canal engineer, and noticed that in the rocks he was cutting through the fossils were always found in a given order from bottom to top, and that the same order appeared at locations on the other side of England. He reasoned that fossils could be used to match and date geological formations, wherever they were found. This principle is still used today.

SIMPLE CELLS

EXPLOSION OF MARINE LIFE
LAND PLANTS
INSECTS
ANIMALS MOVE ONTO LAND
AMPHIBIANS
TROPICAL RAINFORESTS
FLYING INSECTS
REPTILES
MAMMALS
BIRDS
FLOWERING PLANTS
DINOSAURS WIPED OUT
HIMALAYAS FORMED
ANCESTORS OF GREAT APES
MODERN HUMANS
PRESENT DAY

3460
3000
1000
542
470
410
395
360
320
315
225
147
140
65
45
15
0.2

earth's treasury

See thousands of beautiful minerals and gemstones kept here in this tranquil, low-lit gallery. There are multi-coloured crystal groups, minerals that glow in the dark, precious diamonds and nuggets of pure gold, and everyday minerals and rocks that we take for granted. Themed areas explore the processes that created these treasures, and the uses we make of them. Opposite, a dramatic case runs the length of the gallery, crowded with yet more fine specimens.

A rainbow of gems

Natural mineral crystals are often very lovely, like tiny architectural masterpieces. We cut and shape some further as gemstones to enhance their beauty and bring out their vivid colours. The important collection kept at the Museum includes the most valued of these, the rubies, sapphires and emeralds, as well as historic diamond specimens that date back to the first discoveries in South Africa. Other beautiful gemstones, such as fluorite in many colours, may be too soft or fragile to be worn, but are sought after by collectors.

One mineral, many forms

Quartz is natural silica, one of the world's most common minerals. It's found in nearly every geological environment and as part of almost every rock type. It comes in a bewildering variety of colours and shapes, from fine single crystals of purple amethyst and clear rock crystal to gloriously patterned masses of microscopic crystals in agate. Many are prized as ornamental stones and gems.

Everyday treasures

We might place a high value on precious gems and metals, but each mineral and rock has its own special properties, and its own value to us. Dark haematite is our main source of the metal iron. Salt (sodium chloride) flavours our food. Granite is a superbly tough building stone, limestone is more easily carved. Titanium dioxide is the key ingredient in white paint, china clay makes fine porcelain. The rare metal platinum is used not only in jewellery, but also in catalytic converters to remove harmful gases from exhaust fumes. Silica, the commonest rock-forming compound on Earth, has become one of the most important to our lives today. Among many uses, it is the basic ingredient for the glass in our windows, and the raw material for the chips that run our computers.

> Without sand, our computers could not run – it's the raw material for the silicon used to make computer chips.

Oil, the fossil fuel, that shaped the modern world.

More than beautiful

Diamond has value beyond its worth as a gem. It is not only the hardest natural material known, but uniquely combines other properties that make it useful in many ways. For example, it can survive pressures that destroy most other minerals. This property is put to use in a 'diamond anvil', a device that generates extreme pressures by applying a moderate force over a tiny area – the tip of a diamond. Squeezing other minerals between two diamond points allows scientists to study how the minerals would behave under the kinds of pressures found below the surface, deep in Earth's mantle.

human evolution

Our evolutionary story is still incomplete and what evidence exists is fragmented and difficult to read. New discoveries of hominin deepen our understanding, but a single find can sometimes also raise many new questions.

First steps

When the partial skeleton of a small female *Australopithecus afarensis*, an early human relative, was found in Ethiopia in 1974, it captured the world's attention. Lucy, named after the Beatles song *Lucy in the Sky with Diamonds*, was about 3.2 million years old. She had a small brain, long arms and short legs. What marked her out as special was the structure of her knee and hip, which showed that she had routinely walked upright on two legs.

From these first steps, the ancestors of modern human beings evolved: as makers of tools, fire, art and cultures. It was not a simple orderly progression – at times, many different species of early human relatives co-existed with our ancestors, only to die out.

What do you mean, 'human'?

We use the term human to describe all members of the genus *Homo*, from the early larger-brained forms and presumed tool-makers, such as *Homo rudolfensis* and *Homo habilis*, to our own species *Homo sapiens* (usually referred to as modern human).

Museum scientists support the view that *Homo sapiens* evolved in Africa and started to spread across the world from about 100,000 years ago – but that it was not the first human species to spread out of Africa. Who the first migrants were, and what they were like, is one of the hottest debates in human evolution. Most scientists assumed that you needed a big brain and sophisticated tools to be a successful migrant. But, since 1999, five early human skulls, about 1.8 million years old, have been unearthed at Dmanisi, in Georgia. They were hundreds of thousands of years older than anyone expected, their brains were small and they only had simple tools. Arguments continue about their relationship to other early human species.

Closest cousins?

When modern humans eventually reached Europe about 45,000 years ago, they encountered a species that had lived across Europe and western Asia from at least 200,000 years ago. The Neanderthals, as they are known, seem to have lost out to the newcomers, and disappear from the fossil record about 30,000 years ago. Recent research, however, suggests that they may have interbred with our ancestors.

Neanderthals and modern humans are but two of the many branches of the human family tree. Yet another may have been discovered on the Indonesian island of Flores in 2002 and described as a new species, *Homo floresiensis*.

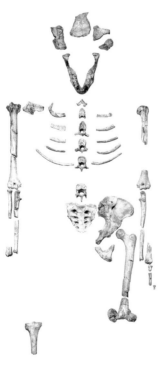

Lucy's skeleton provided clear evidence of apes that walked upright.

 Evolution has shaped our species, just as it has all other living creatures.

Human beings in Britain

When did the first humans settle in Britain? Museum palaeontologists are leading a multi-institutional project to build a picture of Britain's first people, their environment and how they lived. The oldest archaeological evidence shows signs of people in the UK about 900,000 years ago, but the oldest physical remains are about 500,000 years old, from Boxgrove in West Sussex. Bones from horses, deer and rhinos bear the cut-marks of stone tools these people used to butcher the animals. About 100,000 years later, at Swanscombe in Kent, remains of a skull suggest that the evolution of Neanderthals was already underway. They would still be there when the first modern humans arrived about 42,000 years ago.

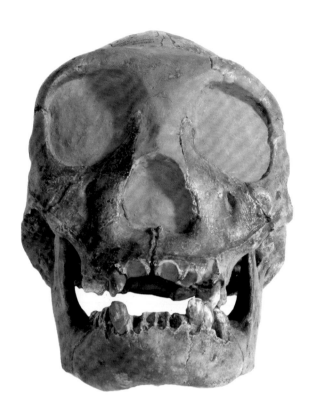

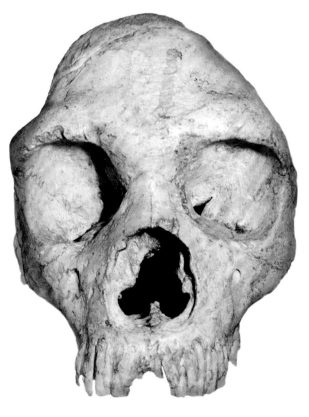

Clockwise from top *Homo erectus*, *Homo neanderthalensis* and *Homo sapiens*.

the natural history museum at tring

We have a sister museum in the Hertfordshire town of Tring, a charming Victorian treasure trove. It lies 50 kilometres northwest of London, just 40 minutes by train, and is a gem of a place to visit. Tring was the family seat of the Rothschilds, a rich banking family, and this delightful museum began as a 21st birthday present to Lionel Walter, son of the First Baron Rothschild. From two cottages in the grounds, it rapidly expanded to fit his growing natural history collections.

A snapshot in time

Visiting Tring today is like stepping back in time. The six galleries are much as Rothschild left them, crowded with specimens from floor to ceiling. Flocks of birds crowd the walls – from the everyday to the exotic, birds of prey and colourful parrots. On the upper floors, elephants, rhinos and a camel parade along the tops of cases, while sharks hang overhead and fishes cover the walls.

By the time of his death in 1937, Rothschild had accumulated the largest collection of animal specimens assembled by one person. He left the building and land to the Natural History Museum, along with hundreds of thousands of specimens, which included both the public displays and the scientific research collections, and a library of 30,000 books. It was one of the most magnificent and important gifts in the Museum's history.

Smaller treasures hide behind wooden doors – dressed fleas and huge stick insects. Gallery 6 is an atmospheric display of more than 700 kangaroos, ostriches, snakes, domestic dogs and champion greyhounds. You'll find wonders such as the platypus, the star-nosed mole and the extinct Tasmanian wolf. Among the many faces peering out of the spotlit cases are some of Rothschild's favourite species, among them the brightly coloured cassowaries and Aldabra giant tortoises. As well as having the permanent galleries, the Museum puts on three temporary exhibitions a year, on topics as diverse as parasites and animal mummies.

The eccentric Rothschild hitched zebras to his carriage, and rode on a giant tortoise.

The collections include a pair of amazing, dressed fleas from Mexico.

Made famous by Darwin

Some of the most famous specimens in the bird collection are finches from the Galapagos Islands, brought back by Charles Darwin and others on the *Beagle* voyage in the 1830s. The specimens, which include this common cactus-finch, *Geospiza scandens*, are known as Darwin's finches. They are now seen as an iconic example of evolution by natural selection, their beaks adapted over time to feed on different sorts of foods. However, Darwin did not recognise their importance at first – in fact he learned more from breeding pigeons back home in England. Seeing how new varieties could be created by selective breeding helped him to realise the power of natural selection in shaping new kinds of living things.

A sanctuary for birds

The bird collection at the South Kensington site was transferred to Tring in the 1970s, where it is now kept in environmentally controlled conditions. Approaching one and a half million specimens, including around 300,000 sets of eggs, the collection represents 95 percent of all known living bird species. Under the care of the Bird Group, this is one of our most actively researched collections, and hundreds of visitors come every year to study here.

The endangered St Vincent parrot, *Amazona guildingii*, is found only on the Caribbean island of St Vincent.

wildlife photographer of the year

Every autumn, we host one of our most popular exhibitions, *Wildlife Photographer of the Year*, showcasing winning entries from our annual competition. Co-owned with BBC Worldwide, *Wildlife Photographer of the Year* is the largest and most prestigious wildlife photographic contest in the world. Receiving over 48,000 entries each year, the competition is open to both amateur enthusiasts and established professionals alike, while the special junior section seeks to encourage and nurture the next generation of aspiring nature photographers.

Through its inspirational photographs the exhibition aims to make people wonder at the splendour and variety of life on Earth. From plant portraits to wildlife in danger, each striking image captures the wild beauty of our planet and reminds us of its fragility. The exhibition also tours the UK and then across six continents, enabling millions of people to wonder at the beauty and majesty of the world around.

Each image in the London exhibition is presented in a contemporary lightbox, a metre-square back-lit frame, which allows the image to glow in the gallery's low lighting to dramatic cinematic effect. Among the categories is a portfolio award for young photographers aged 18 to 26, a wildlife photojournalism award, and an award focusing on the magic of the commonplace – the Urban Environment. The overall winner of the junior section is rewarded with a masterclass with one of the masters of nature photography, whilst the winner of the ultimate accolade, *Wildlife Photographer of the Year*, is rewarded with a prize of £10,000.

Leaping heron by Thomas P. Peschak was Runner-up in the 2009 *Veolia Environnement Wildlife Photographer of the Year* competition.

Pool of hippos by David Fettes was Highly Commended in the 2011 *Veolia Environnement Wildlife Photographer of the Year* competition.

Fading beauty by David Maitland was Specially Commended in the 2011 *Veolia Environnement Wildlife Photographer of the Year* competition.

Desert survivor by Morkel Erasmus was Highly Commended in the 2010 *Veolia Environnement Wildlife Photographer of the Year* competition.

find out more...

Lots of ways to learn

An exciting mix of daily learning opportunities for all visitors is on offer. The *Investigate Centre* encourages visitors to examine natural history specimens as a real scientist might do. Expert facilitators are on hand to help visitors handle, observe and investigate specimens using a large and diverse collection of real objects and scientific tools. In both the Waterhouse and Darwin Centre Cocoon galleries, volunteer facilitators offer engaging activities using specimens and models from the collections. *Nature Live* sessions in the Attenborough Studio bring Museum scientists and the public together to explore the science of nature in a state of the art studio. Regular behind the scenes tours of the Spirit Collections give visitors the chance to get a close look at the scale and processes associated with the collections. Visitors are offered a variety of self-led printed guides and interactive seasonal workshops to learn about the Museum's collections and science. To find out more, visit www.nhm.ac.uk/investigate and www.nhm.ac.uk/naturelive.

Visit our website for:

- Exciting ways to discover the natural world and learn about the cutting-edge science going on here www.nhm.ac.uk.

- NaturePlus (blogs and forums with Museum scientists, news on events and surveys) www.nhm.ac.uk/natureplus.

- For younger visitors, Kids Only offers fun ways to explore the natural world from games and webcams www.nhm.ac.uk/kids-only.

- Imaginative gifts, souvenirs, toys and books inspired by the natural world www.nhmshop.co.uk.

- Visiting information and to book tickets www.nhm.ac.uk/visit-us.

Become a Member

Membership is the best way to enjoy the Museum and its dynamic environment. Great benefits include:

- Free quarterly Museum magazine for adults, *evolve*

- Free quarterly magazine for children, *Wild World*

- Exclusive Members events, including private previews of new exhibitions and discounted tickets for most Museum events

- Free admission and fast-track entry to temporary exhibitions

- 10 free guest tickets to exhibitions (except Child Member category)

- 10 percent discount in most of our shops and restaurants, and 20 percent in the Museum Shop at certain times

- Access to a private Members' Room and free cloakroom

- Behind-the-scenes tours to meet our experts

For further information please call 020 7942 5792/5899, email members@nhm.ac.uk or visit www.nhm.ac.uk/membership.

Support us

The Museum is a recognised charity and the astonishing diversity of Museum activity relies on the outstanding generosity of our supporters, from corporate partnerships and trusts and charitable foundations to our individual donors. Continued funding is crucial if we are to maintain our world-class scientific research collections, offer inspirational exhibitions and provide innovative opportunities to learn more about our planet. There are many ways in which you can support our work, from making a one-off donation of any size to becoming a Patron of the Museum's Annual Fund. Our Patrons play a crucial role and you can join with a minimum donation of £100 and enjoy a variety of benefits. Explore all the options please call 020 7942 5815 or visit our website www.nhm.ac.uk/support.

Become a volunteer

Are you passionate about the planet? Would you like to help us further our important research and educational mission? There are many invaluable ways in which you can participate, from engaging with visitors in the galleries using real specimens to working on collections-related projects in our cutting-edge science departments and libraries, or maintaining and enhancing the Museum's Wildlife Garden. You can share your skills or learn new ones. Experience is not always necessary and training is provided. Call 020 7942 6048 or visit www.nhm.ac.uk/volunteer.

Environmental policies

The Museum is committed to continually improving our environmental performance. We currently produce about 600 tonnes of waste each year. Fifty percent of this is separated for recycling, but our strategy is to reduce the amount we produce in the first place. Our non-drinking water comes from our own borehole, reducing the problem of rising groundwater. Carbon dioxide is the primary greenhouse gas that controls the planet's temperature. In 2005, the Museum's emissions were over 10,000 tonnes. We've committed ourselves to reducing them by 500 tonnes year on year until 2012 with more significant reductions planned until 2020. We installed a highly efficient combined heat and power (CHP) system in 2006 in the central boiler house and we are assessing the carbon impact of any new buildings and refurbishments. To find out more, visit www.nhm.ac.uk/museum-environmental.

Library and Archives

The Museum's Library and Archives are the national reference resource for natural history and the earth sciences. Our collection is the largest in the world and of international importance, with extensive holdings of early books, journals, current literature, artworks, maps and manuscripts. For more information on services, access and opening hours, call 020 7942 5460 or visit www.nhm.ac.uk/library.

Access for all

The Museum aims to offer the widest possible access to our buildings, events, exhibitions and collections. We are committed to broadening our audiences and developing electronic resources to improve access to the information that our collections contains. To find out how we can best accommodate any access requirements please call 020 7942 5000 (during opening hours) or email customerservices@nhm.ac.uk or visit www.nhm.ac.uk/access.

First published by the Natural History Museum, Cromwell Road,
London SW7 5BD

10 9 8 7 6 5 4 3 2

ISBN 978 0 565 09205 4 (English)

A catalogue record for this book is available from the British Library.

Author: Deirdre Janson-Smith
Designer: hat-trick design
Reproduction and printing: Linney Group

FC: Triceratops on display in Dinosaurs at the NHM; IFC © Matt Stuart; p.9 © Hiroshika Setsumasa;
p.23 (b) © John Sibbick/NHMPL; p.26 (l) © Geological Society/NHMPL; pp.28–29 (main) © BrandX
Pictures; p.30 © Matt Stuart; p.34 (bl), p.35 © NHM/Kokoro Model; p.37 (t) © Jack Chant; p.40 © Matt
Stuart; p.44 © Matt Stuart; p.51 © Matt Stuart; p.53 (b) © Geological Society/NHMPL; p.56 (t) © NASA
Goddard Space Flight Center (NASA/GSFC); p.60 (r) © Thomas P. Peschak, (l) © David Fettes; p.61 (t)
© David Maitland, (b) © Morkel Erasmus; p.63 © Matt Stuart; p.64 © Matt Stuart; IBC © Matt Stuart.

All other images are copyright of the Natural History Museum, London, and taken by the Museum's
Image Resources Photographic Unit. For copies of these and other images, contact the Picture Library
at www.nhm.ac.uk/piclib. Every effort has been made to accurately credit all copyright-holders. If we
have been unsuccessful, we apologise and welcome corrections for future editions and reprints.

MIX
Paper from
responsible sources
FSC® C015900

Your *Souvenir Guide*
is fully recyclable